# WE LIKE SCHOOL

By Michaela Muntean
Illustrated by David Prebenna

## A SESAME STREET/READER'S DIGEST KIDS BOOK

Published by Reader's Digest Young Families, Inc.,
in cooperation with Children's Television Workshop

We like school.

stop sign

STOP

swings

slide

seesaw

playground

bus

jungle gym

lunch box

bulletin board

window

map

MAY

| S | M | T | W | T | F | S |
|---|---|---|---|---|---|---|
|  |  |  |  | 1 | 2 | 3 | 4 |
| 5 | 6 | 7 | 8 | 9 | 10 | 11 |
| 12 | 13 | 14 | 15 | 16 | 17 | 18 |
| 19 | 20 | 21 | 22 | 23 | 24 | 25 |
| 26 | 27 | 28 | 29 | 30 | 31 |  |

tape player

calendar

chair

table

desk

I like my classroom.

poster

coat hooks

door

notebook

pencil

paper

desk

SPRING

FALL

I like my desk.

SUMMER

WINTER

plant

pen

apple

rubber
band

book

eraser

I like my teacher.

alphabet

chalkboard

ERNIE
ERNIE
ERNIE
ERNIE

eraser

Ernie and Bert like to write their names.

We like books.

books

Herry Monster likes to paint.

smock

brush

paint

rectangle

circle

triangle

square

scissors

paste

string

Betty Lou likes to make mobiles.

Oscar likes to make a mess.

easel

crayons

fingerpaints

paper

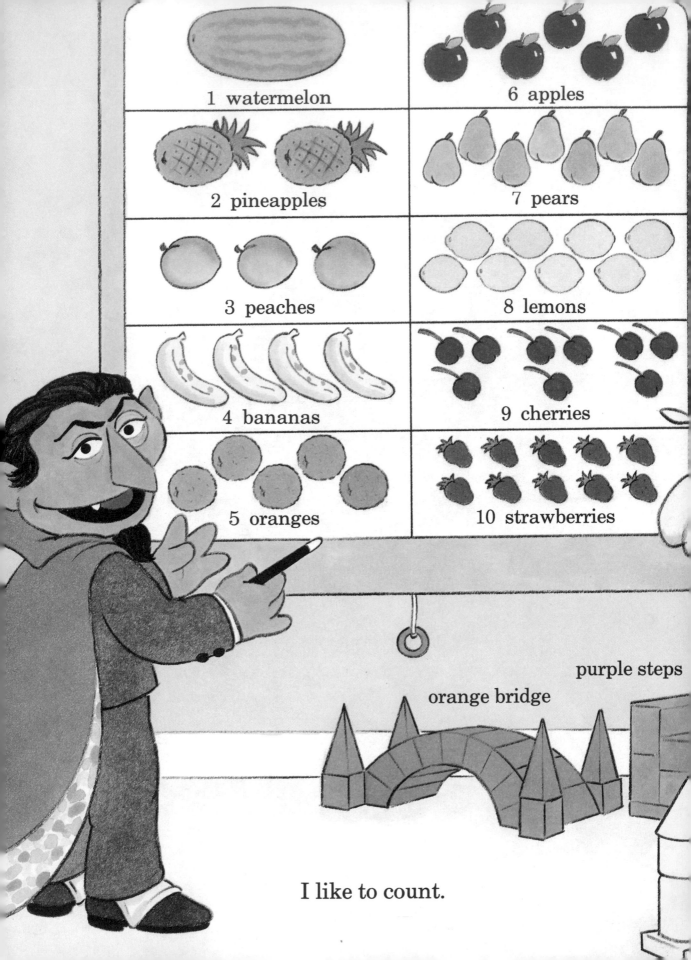

1 watermelon

6 apples

2 pineapples

7 pears

3 peaches

8 lemons

4 bananas

9 cherries

5 oranges

10 strawberries

purple steps

orange bridge

I like to count.

We like to build with blocks.

blue tower

yellow
castle

green fence

red
house

Cookie Monster likes snack time.

cookie

crumbs

raisins

milk

peanuts

plate

carrots

straw

We like music.

cymbals

kazoo

triangle

harmonica

piano

drums

xylophone

tambourine

We like story time.

mat

storybook

pillow

# We like the playground.

ball

slide

hopscotch

jump rope

swing

seesaw

jungle gym

# We like to ride home on the school bus, too!

seat

seat belt

steering
wheel

driver